Phonics and Reading

K

Student Book Three
Lessons 81–120

Author: Pollyann O'Brien, M.A.

Editor: Alan L. Christopherson, M.S.

Alpha Omega Publications • Chandler, Arizona

Horizons Phonics K, Student Book 3
© MM Published by Alpha Omega Publications, Inc. ® All rights reserved
300 North McKemy Avenue, Chandler, Arizona 85226-2618

Horizons is a trademark of Alpha Omega Publications, Inc.
pending registration in the United States Trademark Office.

Printed in the United States of America

ISBN 0-7403-139-X

script

scr

scratch

The consonant blend scr is used at the beginning of a word.

The scr makes the sound we hear at the beginning of scrap.

① Put a circle around each picture that starts with the sound of scr.

| scrap | brush | screw | scratch |

| shrimp | script | scrunch | scram |

381

② **Practice printing Scr with a capital S.**

Scr

③ **Practice printing scr with lower case letters.**

scr

④ **Draw a line from the word to the picture it matches.**

scram

scratch

scrub

scrap

⑤ **Write yes or no to the following questions.**

Can a man scruff?   Can you scrub a smell?

Can you scratch your scalp?   Can you scrub a van?

6 Print the following sentences and add quotation marks to show what
is being said.

Jack said, I can scrub the van.

Pick up that scrap, said Mom.

7 Spell the words below the pictures by writing in the beginning sounds.

_____ ipt   _____ ap   _____ am

8 Read the sentences under the pictures. Put a circle around the sentence that comes last in the story.

Mom had to
open the door.

The pup had to
scratch at the door.

9 Look at the third picture that is added to the story. Put a circle around the sentence that comes last now.

Mom had to
open the door.

The pup had to
scratch at the door.

Mom fed the pup
a dish of milk.

384

1 Circle the letters that make the beginning sounds you hear.

scr sk sl   scr sk sl   scr sk sl   scr sk sl

scr sk sl   scr sk sl   scr sk sl   scr sk sl

sn sm qu   sn sm qu   sn sm qu   sn sm qu

sn sm qu   sn sm qu   sn sm qu   sn sm qu

⭐ **Review: Double Vowels & Blends**

② **Circle the words your teacher reads.**

smell	skillet	slip

snap	scrap	scrub

slap	quit	slept

skid	scream	snip

queen	snail	slide

skit	slip	quit

scrub	sniff	smell

scream	sled	smash

③ **Finish spelling the words by printing the double vowels.**

tr __ __ n   gr __ __ n   sp __ __ k

qu __ __ l   h __ __ t   t __ __ m

4 **Spell the words by printing the beginning sounds.**

ub   ed   ap

unk   een   iff

ide   ap   elt

ail   ip   it

5 **Look at the set of sentences below. Underline the correct sentence to match the picture.**

The queen will ride a bike.   Mr. Smith will slide the team.

The queen will ride on a skunk.   Mr. Smith will speak to the team.

Jean can ride on the slide.   The snail is in the scrub.

Jean can slide on her lap.   The snail is on the trail.

Dean's van is green and white.   Jake likes to skip on the sniff.

Dean's van is bean and whip.   Jake likes to skip near the train.

LESSON 82
Review: Double Vowels & Blends

6 **Finish the sentences by printing words from the word bank.**

| smell | quail | scream | train | snail | deep | chair |

1. I like to ride on a _____ .

2. The skunk can _____ bad.

3. Dean can hop as fast as a _____ can run.

4. Jean said, "The _____ can fly."

5. Did you hear the man _____ ?

6. The queen sat on a _____ .

7. Dave can jump in a _____ lake.

389

7 **Read the sentences under the pictures. Put a circle around the sentence that comes last in the story.**

Mom said, "I see scraps of meat on a plate."

Dad said, "Mom, that was a good meal. I like to eat."

8 **Look at the third picture that is added to the story. Which one would come last now? Put a circle around the sentence that would come last.**

Mom said, "I see scraps of meat on a plate."

Dad said, "Mom, that was a good meal. I like to eat."

Mom said, "I will scrub the dishes and then sit on the bench."

coat

loaf

Review Double Vowel Rule: When two vowels are close together, the first one is long (says its own name) and the second one is silent. Example: bō∅t, tē∅m, bē∉t, trā∕n

1 **Look at the pictures below. Put a circle around the pictures that have the** long ō **sound.**

toast   boat   train   soap

beet   toad   roast   road

2 On the lines below, print the words that match the picture. Cross out the second vowel to show that it is silent and make a straight line over the first vowel to show that it has a long sound.

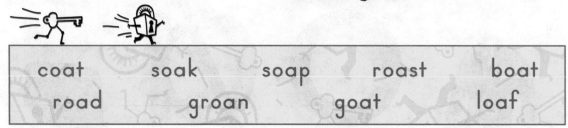

coat   soak   soap   roast   boat

road   groan   goat   loaf

_____

- - - - - - - - - - - - - -

_____

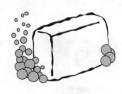

_____

- - - - - - - - - - - - - -

_____

_____

- - - - - - - - - - - - - -

_____

3 **Draw a line from the word to the picture it matches.**

coat

roast

toad

soak

loaf

boat

4 **Print the words that rhyme.**

| coat | road | roast | boat | boast | float | coast |

goat _____ _____

toad _____

toast _____ _____

5 **Read the make-up words.**

boak   toap   fload   joam

6 **Draw a line from the puzzle phrase to the picture it matches.**

a coat on
a boat

a goat
with toast

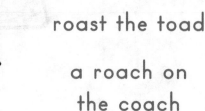

roast the toad

a roach on
the coach

7 **Read the sentences. Draw a line under the one that matches the picture.**

Bill went with us for a ride in a boat.

Bill went with us for a ride on the toast.

Mom can fix a toad for the soap.

Mom can fix a roast for the lunch.

Dave will roach the team.

Dave will coach the team.

Mr. Sloan had a loaf for us.

Mr. Sloan had a groan for us.

8 **Write the sentence.**

My goal is to read well.

froth

frizz

frost

The consonant blend fr is used at the beginning of a word.

The fr makes the sound we hear at the beginning of frog.

① Put a circle around each picture that starts with the sound of fr.

frog   front   fox   fruit

freeze   print   fry   frizz

2 Practice printing Fr with a capital F.

3 Practice printing fr with lower case letters.

4 Draw a line from the word to the picture it matches.

frog

froth

frost

frizz

5 Read the make-up words.

frob   fras   fren   frup   frod

LESSON 84
Beginning Blend fr

6 Print the words that rhyme.

red	Dee	see	cog	log	bee
shy	dog	cry	bed	my	Ted

frog _____

free _____

fry _____

Fred _____

7 Draw a line from the puzzle phrase to the picture it matches.

a sock
on a frog

frost on
a dog

froth on
a moth

Fred with
a frizz

8 **Read the sentences. Print the word from the word bank to complete the sentence.**

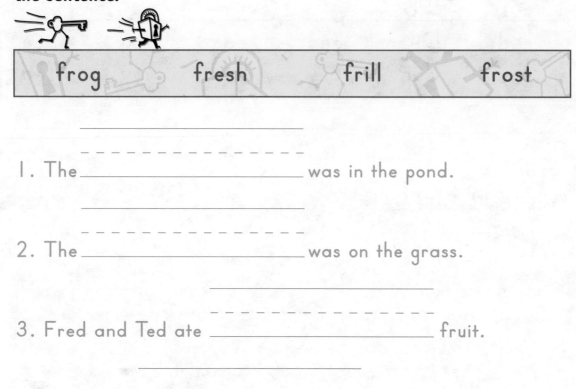

| frog | fresh | frill | frost |

1. The _____ was in the pond.

2. The _____ was on the grass.

3. Fred and Ted ate _____ fruit.

4. Jill had a _____ on her dress.

9 **Read the sentences. Put a circle around the yes if the sentence is true. Circle no if the sentence is not true.**

1. Is a frog as big as a log?   yes   no

2. Is the frost hot?   yes   no

3. Can you drink broth?   yes   no

4. Can you get a note from Mom?   yes   no

10 **Spell the words under the pictures by filling in the beginning sounds.**

og    oke    ass

oth    amp    ip

11 **Write the sentence.**

I am glad I can sit in front.

⑫ **Spell the words under the pictures by filling in the beginning and the ending sounds.**

___ oa ___   ___ oa ___   ___ oa ___

___ oa ___   ___ oa ___   ___ oa ___

LESSON 85
Consonant Ending lt & lf

melt

self

When the consonants lt or lf are together at the end of a word, we blend them together, as in the words melt or self.

1 Put a circle around the pictures that have the sound of lt at the end of the word. Put a square around the pictures that have the sound of lf.

belt   tilt   bell   shelf

self   malt   salt   wilt

2 **You and your teacher can read the sentences together. From the words in the word bank spell the vocabulary words on the lines below.**

| salt | wilt | tilt | belt | shelf | malt |

1. Spell the word if you want something to put around your waist.

2. Spell the word if it goes with pepper to season your food.

3. Spell the word if you want to put something on a special place.

4. Spell the word if a flower does not get enough water.

5. Spell the word if you want something sweet with milk to drink.

6. Spell the word if you want something that is on a slant.

3 **Circle the words your teacher reads.**

| shelf | kilt | lilt |
| melt | make | milk |

| pelt | elf | hilt |
| belt | felt | self |

Consonant Ending lt & lf

4 **Spell the words below the picture by printing the ending sounds**
lf, lt, lk **or** mp.

mi _____   e _____   sa _____

she _____   ra _____   se _____

me _____   si _____   hu _____

la _____   ca _____   wi _____

5 **Read the sentences. Print them on the lines using the correct capital letters at the beginning and for a person's name. Use the correct period or question mark at the end of the sentence.**

did you see an elf

_____

jane has a belt on her dress

_____

_____

the plant will wilt

_____

_____

6 **Look at the pictures below. Underline the correct sentence to match the picture.**

Fred's ice cream cone will melt.
Sam put the lamp on a shelf.

The tot felt sad when she fell.
Ted put on elf pants and socks.

404

lift

soft

left

When the consonants ft are together at the end of a word,
we blend them together, as in the word left.

1 Put a circle around the pictures that have the sound of ft at the end
   of the word.

flag

raft

left

gift

soft

lift

rest

sift

405

2 Print the words for the pictures you circled on the previous page.

raft   left   gift

soft   lift   sift

3 Circle the correct ending for each of the pictures below.

      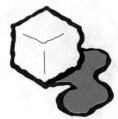

ft nt nd lt lf   ft nt nd lt lf   ft nt nd lt lf

ft nt nd lt lf   ft nt nd lt lf   ft nt nd lt lf

406

4 **Circle the word your teacher reads.**

raft	tent	fond

mend	elf	malt

felt	wilt	soft

sand	tent	shelf

5 **Read the sentences. Underline the sentence that matches the picture.**

The raft was on the pond.

The raft was in the pan.

This is my sand hand.

This is my left hand.

The dress is made of soft cloth.

The lint is made of soft cloth.

Mom had to lift to make the cake.

Mom had to sift to make the cake.

6 **Follow the directions your teacher reads to you.**

7 **Draw a line to the words that match.**

raft   runt

frog   raft

ant   belt

runt   ant

shelf   frog

belt   shelf

1 Circle the letters that make the ending sound you hear.

ck ing nd ch

ck ing nd ch

ck ing nd ch

ck ing nd ch

ck ing nd ch

ck ing nd ch

2 Circle the letters that make the ending sound you hear.

tch nt ng nk lk

tch nt ng nk lk

tch nt ng nk lk

tch nt ng nk lk

tch nt ng nk lk

tch nt ng nk lk

3 **Circle the letters that make the ending sound you hear.**

sk   mp   lf   lt   sk   mp   lf   lt   sk   mp   lf   lt

sk   mp   lf   lt   sk   mp   lf   lt   sk   mp   lf   lt

4 **Circle the letters that make the ending sound you hear.**

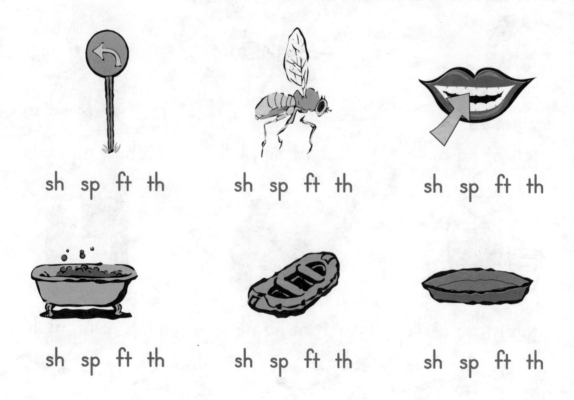

sh   sp   ft   th   sh   sp   ft   th   sh   sp   ft   th

sh   sp   ft   th   sh   sp   ft   th   sh   sp   ft   th

5 **Read the sentences. Choose the correct word to fill in the blanks.**

1. Tom used his _____ hand to print.

left
lift

2. The tot was _____ sick and had the _____.

mumps
pumps

3. Mom can fix the_____ for Jan.

clasp
crisp

4. The hen had ten_____ in her nest.

checks
chicks

5. Jack can _____ his rope.

spell
spin

6. Brent had a _____ at the camp.

ten
tent

6 **Draw a line to the pictures that rhyme.**

game	trick	shake	ear
yell	sail	hear	drip
mail	bell	smell	tell
quick	flame	trip	rake

7 **Circle the words your teacher reads.**

lamp	mask	belt		soft	milk	bunk
bank	runt	gang		ant	hung	pond
tank	raft	silk		limp	melt	self

1 Put a circle around the pictures that have the sound of long ā.

Put a square around the pictures that have the sound of long ē.

maid   peach   train   hear

jail   bead   beach   speak

2 Put a circle around the pictures that have the sound of long ā.

Put a square around the pictures that have the sound of short ă.

pail   rack   paint   pal

rain   cat   chain   Sam

★ Review: Long & Short Vowels

3 Put a circle around the pictures that have the sound of long ē.

Put a square around the pictures that have the sound of short ĕ.

leak	queen	read	red
send	leaf	Ted	met

4 Put a circle around the pictures that have the sound of long ō.

Put a square around the pictures that have the sound of short ŏ.

goat	cot	road	coach
rod	toad	coat	lock

LESSON 88
Review: Long & Short Vowels

_____

- - - - - - - - - - - - - - - - - -

5 Change the word from a short vowel into a word with a long vowel sound by adding a silent e. Example: hŏp hōp̶e̶ hope

hĭd

păl

cŭt

plăn

răt

pĭn

rĭd

415

6 **Print the words in the correct columns.**

rip	hop	rod	Pete	mad	rat
cut	cod	cute	pet	rate	rode
ripe	code	rob	robe	made	hope

Short Vowel Words

_____ _____ _____

- - - - - - - - - - - - - - - - - - - - - - - - - - - - - - - - - - - - - - -

_____ _____ _____

_____ _____ _____

- - - - - - - - - - - - - - - - - - - - - - - - - - - - - - - - - - - - - - -

_____ _____ _____

_____ _____ _____

- - - - - - - - - - - - - - - - - - - - - - - - - - - - - - - - - - - - - - -

_____ _____ _____

Long Vowel Words

_____ _____ _____

- - - - - - - - - - - - - - - - - - - - - - - - - - - - - - - - - - - - - - -

_____ _____ _____

_____ _____ _____

- - - - - - - - - - - - - - - - - - - - - - - - - - - - - - - - - - - - - - -

_____ _____ _____

7 **Print the correct word in the blanks in the sentences.**

1. The sun _____ on the lake.

                                              shone
   stone

2. Dad can fix eggs in the camp _____ .

    dent
    tent

3. Mom said, "Do not _____ ."

    smoke
    snake

4. June is a _____ girl.

    cute
    cube

5. The kids rode on the _____ in the lake.

    tube
    tune

6. Jane ate a big _____ .

    cake
    cane

7. Jan put the bud in a _____ .

    vase
    vane

8. I can _____ in the lake.

    dive
    dime

9. The little kids fuss and _____ .

    whine
    white

417

8 Spell the words under the pictures.

milk

dish

hand

ant

camp

dog

9 Color the picture.

spread

splint

splice

The consonant blend spr is used at the beginning of a word.

The spr makes the sound we hear at the beginning of spring.

1 **Put a circle around each picture that starts with the sound spr.**

spring	sprout	spray	spot
spruce	spread	speak	sprinkle

419

2 **Practice printing** Spr **with a capital** S **and** spr **with a lower case** s.

Spr

spr

The consonant blend spl is used at the beginning of a word.
The spl makes the sound we hear at the beginning of splash.

3 **Put a circle around each picture that starts with the sound** spl.

4 **Practice printing** Spl **with a capital** S **and** spl **with a lower case** s.

Spl

spl

5 **Look at the pictures. Print the correct beginning for each of the words below the pictures.**

spl   spr   spl   spr   spl   spr   spl   spr

spl   spr   spl   spr   spl   spr   spl   spr

6 **Draw a line to match the words in each column. Check each letter.**

spring   split

sprout   splinter

spruce   splice

split   splint

splint   spring

splice   sprout

splinter   spruce

421

7 **Read the sentences. Put quotation marks around the words that show people are speaking.**

Dad said, The spruce tree will get big.

I had a splinter in my hand, said Brad.

Jack said, I can splash you!

Get back! yelled Bill. Jack will splash you!

8 **Print the words in alphabetical order on the lines below.**

spring   think   quick   pink

1. _____ 3. _____

2. _____ 4. _____

9 **Look at the pictures that make a story. Write** | **under the first one,** 2 **under the second one,** 3 **under the third picture, and** 4 **under the last one.**

stand

st

stitch

The consonant blend st is used at the beginning of a word.
The st makes the sound we hear at the beginning of stamp.

1 **Put a circle around each picture that starts with the sound of st.**

step   split   stamp   stick

slide   stump   stitch   stag

423

2 Practice printing St with a capital S and st with a lower case s.

St

st

3 Draw a line from the word to the picture it matches.

step

stand

stunk

sting

stag

4 Read the make-up words.

staj   slod   spug   sprib   splen

5 **Print the words that rhyme.**

| tramp | tilt | crab | wilt | grab | camp |
| rag | kilt | tag | cab | ramp | drag |

stamp _____ _____ _____

stilt _____ _____ _____

stab _____ _____ _____

stag _____ _____ _____

6 **Draw a line from the puzzle phrase to the picture it matches.**

a stag on
the steps

a stamp on
Sam's nose

a dog on stilts

a stunt on
a planet

425

7 **Read the sentences. Print the word from the word bank to complete the sentence.**

stuff	stamp	stick	stack	stuck

1. Jean put a _____ on the mail.

2. Dad had a _____ of notes on his desk.

3. The dog had a _____ to play with.

4. The black van was _____ in the mud.

5. Dan had much _____ on his cot.

8 **Read the sentences. Put a circle around** yes **if the statement is true or could happen. Circle** no **if the statement is not true or could not happen.**

The bee can sting my hand.   yes   no

I can slide on a stem.   yes   no

Jim did a stunt that was fun to see.   yes   no

A skunk can stink.   yes   no

I stand on my hands to sleep.   yes   no

426

sport

batch

gift

1 Circle the letters that make the sound you hear at the end of each word.

tch   sp   ft

tch   sp   ft

tch   sp   ft

tch   sp   ft

tch   sp   ft

tch   sp   ft

tch   sp   ft

tch   sp   ft

427

2 **Print the letters that make the ending sounds you hear.**

she _ _ _

gi _ _ _

wi _ _ _

e _ _ _

me _ _ _

si _ _ _

sa _ _ _

ba _ _ _

ca _ _ _

ba _ _ _

bu _ _ _

ra _ _ _

3 **Read the sentences. Underline the sentence that matches the picture.**

The glass is in a spill.

The ranch is on a hill.

Mom gave a gift to Dad.

Dad gave a sift to Mom.

The bank took Sam to the dimes.

Sam took the dimes to the bank.

Don can grasp the rope.

Don will shelf the rope.

4 **Print the words that rhyme.**

match	lift	dent	sent	hatch	sift

catch _____   _____

bent _____   _____

gift _____   _____

5 You and your teacher can read the sentences together. From the words in the word bank, spell the vocabulary words on the lines below.

| wasp | catch | match | gift | left | grasp |

_____

1. The boy will_____ the ball.

_____

2. The _____ can sting me.

_____

3. I _____ my bat at the game.

_____

4. Sam had a _____ for his mom.

_____

5. Can you_____ the red and black cloth?

_____

6. Meg can _____ the cup.

6 Write the sentence.

I am glad God loves me.

_____

_____

_____

430

fast   st   W west

When the consonants st are together at the end of a word,
we blend them together as in the word fast.

1 Put a circle around the pictures that have the sound of st at the end
of the word.

rest   dust   fast   cast

west   boat   vest   nest

2 **Pick five words from the word bank to print on the lines below.**

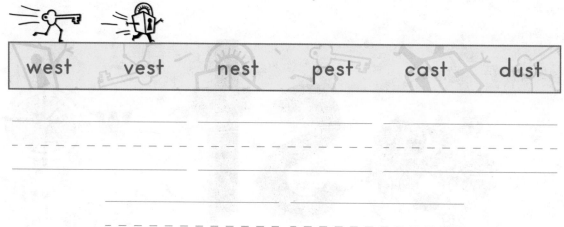

| west | vest | nest | pest | cast | dust |

_____ _____ _____

_____ _____ _____

3 **Circle the correct ending for each of the pictures below.**

st lf ft lt   st lf ft lt   st lf ft lt

st lf ft lt   st lf ft lt   st lf ft lt

4 **Circle the words your teacher reads.**

| fast | elf | tilt | | golf | west | disk |

| wilt | test | sift | | lost | salt | melt |

Consonant Blend Ending st

5 Write the words that rhyme.

| pest | must | cast | dust | last | mast | test | rest | rust |

nest _____ _____

fast _____ _____

just _____ _____

6 Spell the words below by filling in the first two letters.

st   st   st   st

st   st   st   st

1. Your teacher will read the sentence. Find the word from the word bank that will make the sentence correct.

| vest | cast | nest | must | rust | best | west |

1. A place where baby birds hatch is a _____.

2. Doctors fix a broken arm with a _____.

3. A piece of metal that is left in the rain and air will _____.

4. When you really have to do something, we say you _____ do it.

5. A better job than anyone else is the _____.

6. A jacket without sleeves is a _____.

7. The direction in which the sun sets in the evening is the _____.

434

8 Look at the words in the word bank. Print the word on the lines that makes the sentence correct.

cast	fist	rust

1. Jon was mad. He made a _____ with his hand.

2. Ted broke his leg and Dr. Moss fixed it with a _____ .

3. The nail was left out in the rain. We could see the _____ on it.

9 Read the sentences. Put a circle around yes if the statement is true or could happen. Circle no if the statement is not true or could not happen.

Ben felt a lump in his cot.	yes	no
A little red bug is a good gift.	yes	no
Bill had to limp when he had stilts.	yes	no
The cone can melt in the sun.	yes	no
Brent put the belt on his pants.	yes	no

10 **Spell the words under the pictures by filling in the beginning sounds.**

____ amp   ____ ip   ____ ick

____ ag   ____ ump   ____ een

____ ack   ____ ash   ____ og

1 **Put a circle around the pictures that have the ending sound of tch.**

2 **Put a circle around the pictures that have the ending sound of sp.**

③ **Put a circle around the pictures that have the ending sound of** st.

④ **Put a circle around the pictures that have the ending sound of** lt.

⑤ **Circle the words your teacher reads.**

match	slip	fist

list	fast	mist

milk	lisp	spring

quill	lift	mast

LESSON 93
Review: Consonant Endings

6 Put a circle around the pictures that have the ending sound of ft.

7 Spell the words under the pictures by printing the ending sounds.

ca   ma   wi   she

ha   fa   me   e

8 **Print the words that rhyme.**

| munch | patch | lunch | mast | ask | cast | hatch | task |

bunch _____   _____

fast _____   _____

catch _____   _____

mask _____   _____

9 **Read the sentences. Choose the correct word to fill in the blanks.**

fun

1. Jack can run _____.   fast

ranch

2. Don lives on a _____.   rush

match

3. The little chicks will _____ in a week.   hatch

clip

4. Mom made the toast _____.   crisp

440

swing

twins

1 Circle the letters that make the beginning sound you hear.

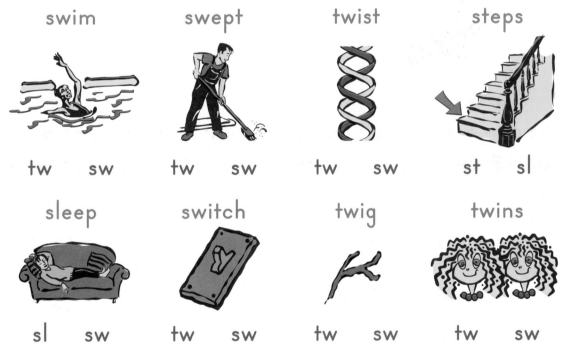

swim	swept	twist	steps
tw sw	tw sw	tw sw	st sl

sleep	switch	twig	twins
sl sw	tw sw	tw sw	tw sw

2 Print the words for the letters you have circled.

sw

tw

441

③ Read the make-up words.

stig twam stel twif

④ Draw a line from the puzzle sentence to the picture it matches.

Jack can swim
on a duck.

The twins will
swing on a dress.

Tom swept
the twig.

⑤ Read the sentences. Put a circle around yes **if the statement is true or could happen. Circle** no **if the statement is not true or could not happen.**

Her hand will swell when it is smashed.	yes	no
You can swim when you stand up.	yes	no
It is fun to play on a swing.	yes	no
All boys and girls are twins.	yes	no

442

6 **Look at the pictures below. Choose the word from the word bank that tells about the picture.**

| twins | swim | swift | swing |

1. Ben will _____ across the lake.

2. The boys and girls can have fun on the _____ .

3. Meg and Greg are _____ .

4. The train on the rail is _____ .

7 Spell the words under the pictures by filling in the beginning sounds you hear.

___ing   ___ins   ___ept

___ig   ___ift   ___itch

8 Print the sentence.

I like to swing on a swing.

LESSON 95
Review: Consonant Beginnings

1 Choose the correct beginning consonant blend for the pictures below.

tw　spr　st　　tw　spr　st　　tw　spr　st　　tw　spr　st

tw　spr　st　　tw　spr　st　　tw　spr　st　　tw　spl　st

spl　sp　qu　　spl　sp　qu　　spl　sp　qu　　tr　tw　st

spl　sp　sn　　spl　sp　qu　　tw　sk　qu　　spl　sk　qu

445

❷ **Circle the words your teacher reads.**

twin	twist	tweet

step	stiff	staff

sprig	spring	spruce

slash	splash	sting

quilt	quit	quiz

spin	speed	spank

❸ **Read the sentences. Choose the correct word from the word bank to fill in the blanks.**

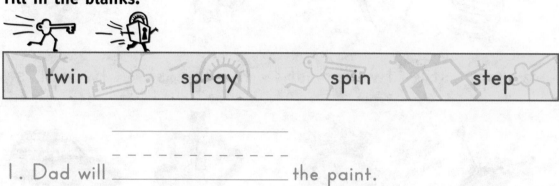

twin	spray	spin	step

1. Dad will _____ the paint.

2. Jed and Ted are _____ boys.

3. I can _____ on the rocks.

4. Beth has a top that can _____.

4 **Print the words that rhyme.**

| spin | tray | crash | flit | trash | thin | sit | pray |

twin _____   _____

splash _____   _____

spray _____   _____

quit _____   _____

5 **Read the sentences. Put a circle around** yes **if the statement is true or could happen. Circle** no **if the statement is not true or could not happen.**

Bob is ten years old. Jeff is six.

They are twins.   yes   no

Ben and Jeff went to splash in the mud.

They are clean.   yes   no

Beth and Meg drink milk.

They had a good lunch.   yes   no

The queen sat on a soft bench.

She was happy with her staff.   yes   no

447

6 Spell the words under the pictures by printing the beginning blend sound.

_____ een   _____ ash   _____ ay

_____ ill   _____ it   _____ int

7 Print each set of words in alphabetical order.

twist   quiz   spin

1. _____   2. _____   3. _____

sprint   mint   prize

1. _____   2. _____   3. _____

8 Print the words in alphabetical order.

gift   dash   speak

1._____   2._____   3._____

9 Look at the sentences below. Underline the correct sentence to match the picture.

Sean will catch the ball.
Sean will hatch the ball.

The clasp will sting you.
The wasp will sting you.

Frank can run fast on the path.
Frank can run much on the path.

449

10 **Print the following sentences. Put quotation marks around the words that show someone is talking.**

Jack said, I like to swim.

- -

- -

Please come here, said the queen.

- -

- -

What time is it? asked Clay.

- -

- -

1 **Circle the correct ending blend for the pictures below.**

lf ft ng nk

lf ft ng nk

lf ft ng nk

lf ft ng nk

lf ft ng nk

lf ft ng nk

lk lp sk sh

lk lp sk sh

lk lp sk sh

lk lp sk sh

lk lp sk sh

lk lp sk sh

⭐

② **Read the sentences. Choose the correct word from the word bank to fill in the blanks.**

shelf	milk	sink	skunk	bush	silk

1. I put my caps on a _____ .

2. Jan's dress _____
   is made of _____ cloth.

3. Dad put _____
   the dish in the _____ .

4. Fred saw a _____
   on the road.

5. Jan said,
   "I like to drink _____ ."

6. The green _____
   has one more leaf.

452

LESSON 96
Review: Consonant Endings

3 Spell the words under the pictures by filling in the ending blends.

sku

de

di

he

ri

ba

dri

mi

le

ma

sa

chi

453

4 Read the sentences below. Put a circle around could be if the statement could happen. Put a circle around no way if it is something you would not want to happen.

I want to have a skunk in my bed.　　could be　no way

Jack wants a glass of milk.　　could be　no way

Jan has a dish in her ear.　　could be　no way

The shelf has lots of hats.　　could be　no way

I like to help my dad.　　could be　no way

5 Print these words in alphabetical order.

| left | spin | apple | fish |

1. _____　3. _____

2. _____　4. _____

454

6 **Print the words that have the same ending blends in a row.**

shelf	think	mask	raft	drift	milk
flask	sang	fang	elf	sank	silk

lf

ft

ng

nk

sk

lk

455

7 **Read the sentences with your teacher. From the words in the word bank, print the vocabulary word that describes the sentence.**

skunk	fang	think	silk	elf	milk

1. An animal that stinks is in the bush. _____

2. A soft kind of cloth used to make a dress. _____

3. The teeth are very sharp. _____

4. When you use your brain, you do this. _____

5. Something white to drink. _____

6. A little person in make-up stories. _____

farm

market

When a word has ar in it, it makes the sound we hear in car.

It can be used at the beginning of a word as in arch,

or in the middle of the word as in market.

1 Put a circle around the pictures that have the sound of ar in them.

cart　　　　spring　　　　car　　　　barn

star　　　　fast　　　　market　　　　farm

② **Practice printing words with ar in them. Underline the ar in each word.**

star
_____

part
_____

bar
_____

spark
_____

arm
_____

market
_____

③ **Read the sentences. Draw a line from the picture to match the sentence. Underline all the words that have ar in them.**

Carl and I like
to ride in a cart.

Dar had a party
for the kids.

The shark has
sharp teeth.

We saw a spark
from the fire.

④ **Print the words from the word bank on the lines next to the word they rhyme with.**

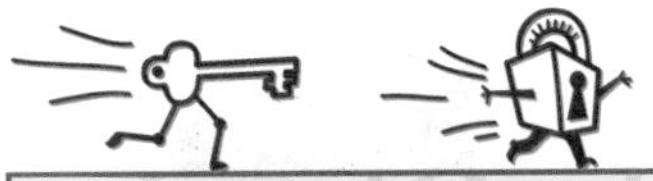

charm	mark	jar	lard	farm	lark
chard	far	shark	harm	hard	Dar

car

dark

card

arm

⑤ **Read the make-up words.**

kark   chark   gark   jark

459

6 Draw a line from the puzzle phrase to the picture it matches.

a car on
a barn

a shark in
the cat dish

a dog with
an arm

a farm
on a jar

7 Find the words in the word search. Circle the words that go across.
Circle the words that go down.

Across	Down
park shark farm	dark arm star

```
L I N O C D Q X
V U Y X P A R K
A B M W E R J D
C S H A R K G J
O T W R L V U L
F A R M G E B S
T R G L E Z I V
B Q I M Y B P Q
```

shore

or

fork

When a word has or in it, it makes sound we hear in the middle of corn. It can be used at the beginning of a word as in order, or at the end of a word as in for.

1 Put a circle around the pictures that have the sound of or in them.

fork   shore   cork   stork

horse   horn   thorn   orchard

461

2 **Practice printing words with or in them. Underline the or in each word.**

horn

sport

fork

shore

thorn

dorm

3 **Read the sentences. Draw a line from the picture to match the sentence. Underline all the words that have or in them.**

Norm has a
torch in his hand.

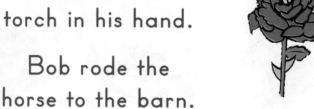

Bob rode the
horse to the barn.

Put the fork
by the plate.

The rose has
thorns on the stem.

462

4 Draw a line from the puzzle phrase to the picture it matches.

a cork on
a thorn

a short stork

a horn in
a storm

a cord on
a fork

5 Read the make-up words.

corb   stort   dort   lorf

6 Print the sentences below. Be sure to use a capital letter at the beginning and a period or question mark at the end.

the thorn was sharp

did the man honk the horn on the car

463

7 **Read the sentences with your teacher. From the word bank, print the vocabulary word that tells about the sentence.**

orchard	cork	dorm	thorns
morning	stork		pork

1. The alarm clock rings first thing in the day. _____

2. The roses have sharp points on the stems. _____

3. Many people live there to go to school. _____

4. A bird that has long legs and can fly fast. _____

5. This is put in the top of a bottle. _____

6. This is what we call the meat from a pig. _____

7. Fruit trees are planted together. _____

464

8 **Read the sentences. Choose the correct word from the word bank and print it in the blanks.**

orchard	cord	storm	sport
sort	scorch	forks	

1. The tree fell down in a strong _____.

2. The sun may _____ the plant on this hot day.

3. We put a short _____ on the cart.

4. Football is a good _____ for kids.

5. Did you _____ out the _____?

6. Apple trees are planted in an _____.

465

9 **Read the sentences with your teacher. From the words in the word bank, print the vocabulary word that tells about the sentence.**

| barn | arms | farm | shark | cart | jar |

1. A wagon that could be big or little.

2. Place where animals are kept.

3. A place where you could see a big building.

4. You have two of these on your body.

5. A big fish in the sea that has sharp teeth.

6. A place to put food.

sport

ar or

fork

1 Choose the correct vowel plus r for the sound you hear in the pictures.

ar   or   ar   or   ar   or   ar   or

ar   or   ar   or   ar   or   ar   or

2 **Print the words below the pictures. Put a circle around the words that have ar in them. Underline the words that have or in them.**

corn

dart

shark

horse

stork

spark

thorn

north

sharp

3 **Read the sentences. Choose the correct word from the word bank to fill in the blanks.**

| card | lark | spark | torn | horse | horn |

1. There was a _____ from the fire.

2. The boys and girls can ride the _____ .

3. Mom had _____ her dress.

4. The _____ sang a pretty song.

5. Dad had a _____ on his truck to toot.

6. Carl sent a birthday _____ to Norm.

4 **Circle the words your teacher reads.**

cart	barn	fort

born	charm	shark

farm	sport	pork

horse	dart	jar

5 **Spell the words under the pictures with or or ar.**

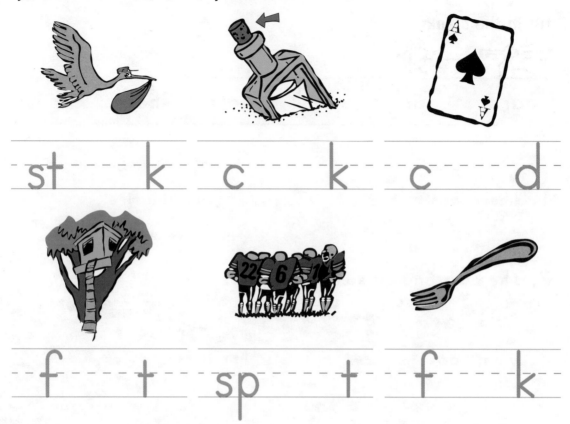

st __ k   c __ k   c __ d

f __ t   sp __ t   f __ k

6 **Read the sentences below. Put a circle around could be if the statement could happen. Put a circle around no way if it is something you would not want to happen.**

The sharks swim in the sea.   could be   no way

We ate lunch with a cork.   could be   no way

It is fun to live on a farm.   could be   no way

Dan and Jim had a good card game.   could be   no way

We will park the car in the barn.   could be   no way

We eat pork that comes from a rat.   could be   no way

7 **Read the sentences with your teacher. From the words in the word bank, print the vocabulary word that tells about the picture.**

art	barn	horse	scorch	thorn

1. Men use a brush
   to paint pictures.

2. We like to ride
   this animal.

3. A sharp point on
   a rose can hurt
   your arm.

4. Do not use too hot
   an iron to press
   your dress.

5. A farm building
   that is a good
   place for animals.

471

8 **Put the words in alphabetical order.**

card born dark	pork horse barn

1._____   1._____

2._____   2._____

3._____   3._____

9 **Color the picture.**

472

shark   **ar**   barn

① **Put a circle around the pictures that have the sound of** *ar* **in them.**

Underline the *ar* **in each word.**

dart   jar   park   catch

star   brush   yarn   march

473

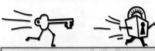

2 Spell the correct word under each picture. Then print the rest of the words on the lines.

charm	market	hard	marsh	lark
barn	shark		arm	star

_____   _____   _____

- - - - - - - - - -   - - - - - - - - - -   - - - - - - - - - -

_____   _____   _____

- - - - - - - - - -   - - - - - - - - - -   - - - - - - - - - -

_____   _____   _____

- - - - - - - - - -   - - - - - - - - - -   - - - - - - - - - -

3 Read the make-up words.

karb   jarb   darf   slark

4 Circle the word your teacher reads.

alarm	mark	hark

market	marsh	charm

star	cart	farm

mart	darn	march

474

5 **Choose the correct word to finish each sentence and write it in the blank.**

cart

1. We rode to the barn in a _____ .   farm

star

2. Mark saw a _____ in the sky.   dark

arm

3. The _____ clock was set for six.   alarm

hark

4. The big dog will _____ at cars.   bark

farm

5. The horse lives on a _____ .   charm

market

6. Mom will buy food at the _____ .   jacket

6 **Draw a line from the picture to match the sentence. Underline all the words that have ar in them.**

The horse will
trot to the barn

Tom is a short boy.

We can play on
the bars in the park.

Ted's dog, Spot, will
bark at the cats.

475

7 **Draw a line from the puzzle phrase to the picture it matches.**

a park on a cart

a shark on a chart

a card in a jar

a star on his arm

8 **Read the sentences with your teacher. From the words in the word bank, print the vocabulary word that tells about the sentence.**

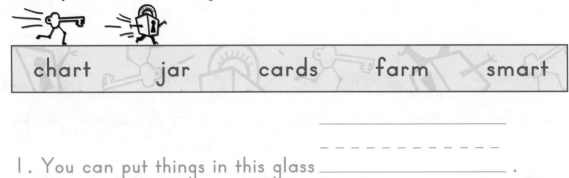

chart   jar   cards   farm   smart

1. You can put things in this glass _____ .

2. We played a game with some _____ .

3. Clark put the horses in a barn on the _____ .

4. You use your brain and are very _____ .

5. The teacher put a note on a _____ .

torn

or

horn   fork

1 **Put a circle around the pictures that have the sound of or in them.**
Underline the or in each word.

corn   park   cord   skunk

storm   horse   porch   stork

2 **Spell the correct word below each picture.**

stork   fork   corn   horn

3 **Print the words from the word bank on the lines below.**

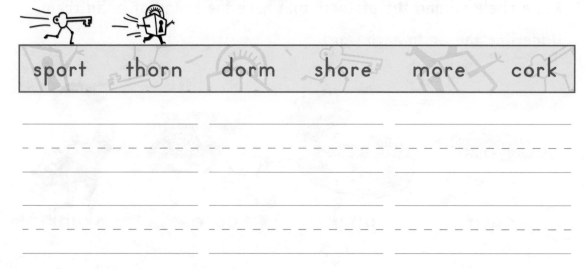

sport   thorn   dorm   shore   more   cork

4 **Put a circle around the words you find in the puzzles.**

Across: cord   **Across:** market, torn   **Across:** dorm, sort
Down: pork   **Down:** dart   **Down:** horse, morn

B P W Y   B D S A P B   F H Z A K
C O R D   M A R K E T   D O R M Q
A R N G   Y R C W Q M   H R P O L
X K M C   P T O R N Z   M S O R T
                                      A E D N B

478

_____

5 **Choose the correct word to finish each sentence and print it in the blank.**

1. A wind _____ broke the branch.   stork
                                                storm

2. Mom can fix a lunch with _____ .   corn
                                                 cork

3. We saw the long legs on the _____ .   fork
                                                    stork

4. For dinner, we had a _____ roast.   park
                                                  pork

5. The rose stem has a sharp _____ .   snort
                                                  thorn

6. Dad put a _____ in the bottle.   cork
                                               star

7. We ate some cake and wanted _____ .more   more
                                                        morn

6 **Circle the words your teacher reads.**

| fort | short | pork | | north | dorm | fork |
| cork | sworn | more | | horn | cord | corn |

7 Read the sentences. Put a circle around yes if the statement is true or could happen. Circle no if the statement is not true or could not happen.

I think cork is good to eat.   yes   no

It is good to have a horse to ride.   yes   no

We need to live in a storm.   yes   no

We will ride in a cart more than

300 miles.   yes   no

The thorn from a rose is what
I want in my hand.   yes   no

It is fun to do art work.   yes   no

8 Print the words in alphabetical order.

horn short dorm more   cork sort Ford north

1.   1.

2.   2.

3.   3.

4.   4.

480

er church

ir

shirt ur serve

When a word has er, ir or ur, it has the sound we hear in fern.

Study the sounds in the words her, fir and turn.

They all make the same sound with the r.

1. Look at the words that have the sound of er as in her.

1. Put a circle around the words that are spelled with er.

2. Underline the ir words.

3. Put a square around the ur words.

bird	fur	shirt	swerve	verse
clerk	nurse	jerk	surf	bur
church	blur	burg	her	spur

481

2 Circle all the words that have the er sound as in her and are spelled with er.

perch   loaf   Ted   fern   Bert

jerk   herd   this   rent   serve

3 Practice printing the correct word below each picture.

perch

Bert

herd

berth

nerve

serve

Gert

stern

4 Read the make-up words.

terb   derp   ler   jerj

⑤ **Read the sentences. Draw a line from the picture to match the sentence. Underline all the words that have an er sound in them and are spelled with the letters er.**

The green fern
is a plant.

A herd of cattle
ate the grass.

A rope could jerk
from your hands.

⑥ **Read the sentences below. Put a circle around** could be **if the statement could happen. Put a circle around** no way **if it is something you would not want to happen.**

Kirk can put on his shirt.   could be   no way

All boys like to wear blue skirts.   could be   no way

I learned the third verse from

the Bible.   could be   no way

It is fun to twirl a rope.   could be   no way

I am thirty years old today.   could be   no way

7 **Read the sentences with your teacher. From the word bank, print the vocabulary word that tells about the picture.**

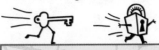

| verse | herd | hers | stern |

Merv went to see
a group of cattle.

_____

- - - - - - - - - - - -

_____

Bert should read
a part of the Bible.

_____

- - - - - - - - - - - -

_____

The clerk looks cross
and has no smile.

_____

- - - - - - - - - - - -

_____

The coat belongs
to the girl.

_____

- - - - - - - - - - - -

_____

8 **Look at the words that end with the letters er and make the same sound. Underline the er in each word.**

| mother | sister | brother | butter |

| banker | camper | hunter | singer |

9 **Read the sentences below. Put a circle around** could be **if the statement could happen. Put a circle around** no way **if it is something you would not want to happen.**

Bert should jerk her arm.   could be   no way

All horses like to perch in a tree.   could be   no way

I like to learn the verse from

the Bible.   could be   no way

The herd of sheep likes to live

on a boat.   could be   no way

There are many herbs you can eat.   could be   no way

10 **Draw a line from the puzzle phrase to the picture it matches.**

a dog in
a fern

a cat
that jerks

corn on
a perch

swerve into
a stump

485

11 Read the sentences with your teacher. From the words in the word bank, print the vocabulary words that tell about the sentence.

morning	short	stork	cork	cord	pork

1. A big white bird with long legs was on the lake.

_____

2. I got out of bed when the alarm rang early.

_____

3. Mark has a coat that is not as long as he wants it.

_____

4. We put a top in the bottle so it would not spill.

_____

5. The meat that Mom fixed for dinner came from a pig.

_____

6. The string was put on a lamp so we could turn it on.

_____

486

bird

ir

shirt

whirl

When a word has er, ir or ur, it has the sound we hear in bird.

Study the sounds in the words her, bird and turn.

They all make the same sound with the r.

1 Look at the words that have the sound of ir as in fir.

1. Put a circle around the words that are spelled with ir.

2. Underline the er words.

3. Put a square around the ur words.

bird	fir	shirt	nerve	verse
quirk	dirt	perk	turf	firm
church	birth	hers	skirt	purr

2 **Circle all the words that have the ir sound as in bird and are spelled with ir.**

squirt   thirst   birth   stir   short

shirt   Dirk   flirt   ship   smirk

3 **Practice printing the correct word below each picture.**

bird   third   dirt   chirp

smirk   whirl   first   fir

4 **Read the make-up words.**

birb   dirp   mib   jirj

⑤ **Read the sentences. Draw a line from the picture to match the sentence. Underline all the words that have the ir sound in them and are spelled with the letters ir.**

The green fern
is a plant.

The number three is
called the third one.

A smirk is not
a good smile.

Gert's skirt is green.

⑥ **Draw a line from the puzzle phrase to the picture it matches.**

a dog with
a skirt

a cat who
has a shirt

a bird in
a whirl

dirt on
a porch

489

7 **Read the sentences with your teacher. From the word bank, print the vocabulary word that tells about the picture.**

| bird | girl | third | smirk |

The hat is hers.

The feathers of this little one are yellow.

Mom told her three times.

The smile is not a nice one.

8 **Circle the words your teacher reads.**

| bird | shirt | fern |

| birch | first | third |

| cart | birth | skirt |

| chirp | sir | dirt |

490

curl

turkey

purr

church

When a word has er, ir or ur, it has the sound we hear in burn.

Study the sounds in the words her, fir and burn.

They all make the same sound with the r.

① Look at the words that have the sound of ur as in burn.

1. Put a circle around the words that are spelled with ur.

2. Underline the ir words.

3. Put a square around the er words.

shirk	fur	shirt	surf	clerk
purse	nurse	jerk	Turk	bur
burn	curl	hurl	church	burst

② Circle all the words that have the ur sound as in burn and are spelled with ur.

turn   perch   loaf   surf   churn

curse   smirk   herd   purse   curl

③ Practice printing the correct word below each picture.

spur

purple

turkey

curve

purse

Curt

fur

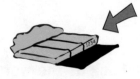
curb

④ Read the make-up words.

furb   gurp   murd   kurf

492

5 **Read the sentences. Draw a line from the picture to match the sentence. Underline all the words that have the ur sound in them and are spelled with the letters ur.**

The nurse had her hand in her purse.

The ball can burst if you kick it hard.

Turk is so big he can hurdle the gate.

6 **Draw a line from the puzzle phrase to the picture it matches.**

fur on a bird

a dog who can purr

a cat in a purse

a churn in the surf

7 Read the sentences with your teacher. From the word bank, print the vocabulary word that tells about the picture.

| purr | fur | burst | churn |

The cub's coat is black and white.

The kitten tells us he is happy.

Butter has to whirl to be made.

He broke the ball by hitting it too hard.

8 Look at the words that end with the letters er and make the same sound. Underline the er in each word.

bumper   surfer   buster   duller

upper   muster   bluster   junker

skirt

fern

purse

1 **Put a circle around the pictures that have the same sound as the words** Bert, shirt, **or** surf.

shark

cart

burn

burst

twirl

short

bird

third

② **Choose the correct word to complete the sentence.**

1. The green _____ was on the porch.　flirt　fern

2. We were the _____ ones in line.　first　frost

3. The _____ came over the shore.　surf　soft

4. The chick will _____ on the gate.　scorch　perch

5. The baby _____ will chirp in the nest.　bur　bird

6. The _____ can help Turk take his pills.　nerve　nurse

③ **Print the words that rhyme.**

| her | lurk | flirt | fur | perk | Bert |

Kirk _____　_____

hurt _____　_____

stir _____　_____

4 **Practice printing the correct word below each picture.**

shirt

herd

fern

church

purse

skirt

5 **Read the sentences. Draw a line from the picture to the sentence it matches. Underline all the words that have an er, ir or ur sound in them.**

He hit a nerve in his hand and it hurt.

The bird will take a bath in the birdbath.

The birch tree is big.

We slept in the berth on the train.

497

6 **Print the words from the word bank in columns below.**

squirt	perch	herd	lurch	stir
jerk	birth	term	birch	fur

er	ir	ur

7 **Circle the words your teacher reads.**

bird	shirt	skirt

purr	furr	stir

herd	whirl	dirt

churn	burst	fern

8 **Read the sentences. Choose the correct word from the word bank to fill in the blanks.**

| birth | shirts | squirt | bird | purse | clerk | herd |

1. Gert is a _____ at the store.

2. The soda pop will _____ all over us.

3. They told us about the _____ of baby Jesus.

4. The boys put on their pants and _____.

5. The _____ of goats liked the green grass.

6. The girl had a red _____ to hold her money.

7. The yellow _____ made a nest in the birch tree.

9 **Read the sentences below. Put a circle around** could be **if the statement could happen. Put a circle around** no way **if it is something you would not want to happen.**

The kitten hid under the porch.   could be   no way

The surf is too big so we can not swim.   could be   no way

Turk, my brother, has fur on

his back.   could be   no way

Mom had to urge me to get up

this morning.   could be   no way

10 **Draw a picture and color it. Tell your teacher about the picture.**

carp

corn

ar or

barn

1 **Put a circle around the words that have the sound of or in them.**

Underline the or in each word.

sport   horse   thorn   cart

farm   storm   dorm   cork

501

② Put a circle around all the pictures that have the sound of ar in them. Underline the ar.

park   dart   stork   barn

cord   shark   lark   spark

③ Print the words in alphabetical order.

starch   lark   arch

1._____   2._____   3._____

pork   carp   bar

1._____   2._____   3._____

star   bark   porch

1._____   2._____   3._____

4 **Choose the correct word to complete the sentences.**

1. Norm can paint the _____ for the chart.

art
cart

2. The boat came to the _____ of the lake.

shore
sore

3. When were you _____ ?

born
barn

4. Dan and Mike can be _____ .

partners
parkers

5. Mom made a coat out of red _____ .

yard
yarn

6. The _____ can bite.

shark
sharp

7. A _____ is a fish that swims in the lake.

carp
cart

8. Mark can _____ when he sleeps.

snore
thorn

9. We put the hens in the _____ .

yard
hard

503

5 **Draw a line from the picture to the sentence it matches.**

Barb rides a
horse named Star.

Merle puts a
note on the chart.

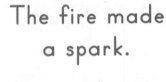

The fire made
a spark.

The baby was
born in the barn.

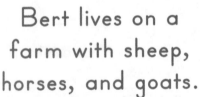

Mom can darn
my socks.

Bert lives on a
farm with sheep,
horses, and goats.

6 **Read the sentences. Put a circle around** yes **if the statement is true or could happen. Circle** no **if the statement is not true or could not happen.**

A lark is a pretty bird.	yes	no
We can play in a park.	yes	no
A star can sing all day.	yes	no
Corn is good to eat.	yes	no

LESSON 106
Review: Vowels Plus r; ar, or

7 Print the words in columns.

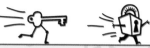

| porch | arch | corn | scorch | more |
| score | dart | charm | scarf | start |

ar   or

_____   _____

_____   _____

_____   _____

_____   _____

_____   _____

_____   _____

8 Read the sentences. Put a circle around yes if the statement is
true or could happen. Circle no if the statement is not true or could
not happen.

It is fun to have a sore arm.   yes   no

A dog can purr.   yes   no

A horn must have a scarf.   yes   no

505

9 Print the words that rhyme.

| farm | core | cork | thorn | pork | scorn |
| torn | fork | harm | tore | sore | charm |

arm _____ _____ _____

born _____ _____ _____

stork _____ _____ _____

more _____ _____ _____

1 **Put a circle around the pictures that have the er sound as in Gert, turf or shirt.**

2 **Put a circle around the pictures that have the or sound as in born.**

3 **Put a circle around the pictures that have the ar sound as in park.**

4 **Put the words in alphabetical order.**

stork   fork   farm

1._____   2._____   3._____

burst   car   arm

1._____   2._____   3._____

5 **Choose the correct word to complete the sentence.**

1. The _____ of the game was 7 to 3. score scorn

2. We had to _____ the car. start stork

3. Dad can _____ his horn. honk hang

4. The nurse put the pills in her _____. purse dark

5. The rider used his _____ on the horse. spur spurt

6. Barb _____ her pretty dress to church. wore scarf

7. All the goats were put in the _____. barn born

6 **Print the words that rhyme.**

| park | core | lark | chore | perch | churn |
| lurch | burn | church | dark | store | fern |

bark _____ _____ _____

birch _____ _____ _____

more _____ _____ _____

turn _____ _____ _____

7 **Draw a line between the word and the picture it matches.**

corn

park

stork

skirt

purse

fern

510

LESSON 108
Plurals:  s

Rule: Most words will show plurals (or more than one)
by adding s to the root (main) word as in
boy - boys; pet - pets.

① **Put a circle around the pictures that show plurals (or more than one in that picture).**

511

2 Spell the words beside each picture. If there is more than one object in the picture, print an s at the end of the word.

I can   2 — — — — — —

I cake   3 — — — — — —

I bat   4 — — — — — —

I hand   2 — — — — — —

I cap   3 — — — — — —

512

③ **Draw a line from the phrase to the picture it matches.**

three pigs

one frog

two sleds

three gifts

one duck

five chicks

④ **Choose and print the correct word to complete the sentence.**

1. Jack has two _____ for pets.

cat
cats

2. Mike saw three _____ in the yard.

rat
rats

3. One _____ was near the lake.

duck
ducks

4. Three _____ were in the nest.

bird
birds

5. One _____ is on the desk.

cup
cups

513

5 **Fill in both blanks.**

_____

- - - - - - - - - -

Dad had one _____, and

_____

- - - - - - - - - -

Mom had two _____.   1 pen   2 pens

_____

- - - - - - - - - -

Greg takes one _____,

_____

- - - - - - - - - -

Tom takes three_____.   1 pill   3 pills

_____

- - - - - - - - - -

Bill has two _____, but

_____

- - - - - - - - - -

I have one _____.   1 dog   2 dogs

_____

- - - - - - - - - -

Jim has one red _____,

_____

- - - - - - - - - -

but Tim has three_____.

1 van   3 vans

6 Choose the correct phrase to match the picture. Print the words under the picture.

one pig
two dogs
three horses

four frogs
one dog
two cats

six caps
two cups
one hat

one lake
three logs
two crabs

7 **Draw a line from the picture to the sentence it matches.**

The boxer was in the
ring to start the match.

Barb put the butter on
the table for dinner.

My mother and father
go to church on Sunday.

Herb can hear the
buzzer at the door.

The red car is a better
car than the green one.

Fern put the paper
on the chart.

We had the joker in
the deck of cards.

Kerr is a
good singer.

516

Rule: To make plurals for root words which end in s, ss, ch, sh and x, add es. Example: bus - buses, dress - dresses, lunch - lunches, fish - fishes, box - boxes.

① **Put a circle around the pictures that are plural (or more than one).**

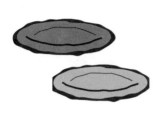

2 Spell the words beside each picture. If there is more than one object in the picture, print an es at the end of the word.

1 box   2 _____

1 fox   4 _____

1 glass   3 _____

1 ax   2 _____

1 fish   3 _____

LESSON 109
Plurals: es

3 **Draw a line from the phrase to the picture it matches.**

five bunches

three watches

two axes

one kiss

two inches

two boxes

4 **Choose and print the correct word to complete the sentence.**

1. Mom wanted to mail two _____ to Jan.

box
boxes

2. There were three _____ of grapes.

bunch
bunches

3. Bill had one _____ from his mom.

kiss
kisses

4. Jane has three pretty _____ .

dress
dresses

5. There were two _____ on the desk.

lunch
lunches

5 **Fill in both blanks.**

Bill rode one _____ , but

Jean rode three _____ .

1 bus   3 buses

Peg broke four _____ .

Nan broke two more _____ .

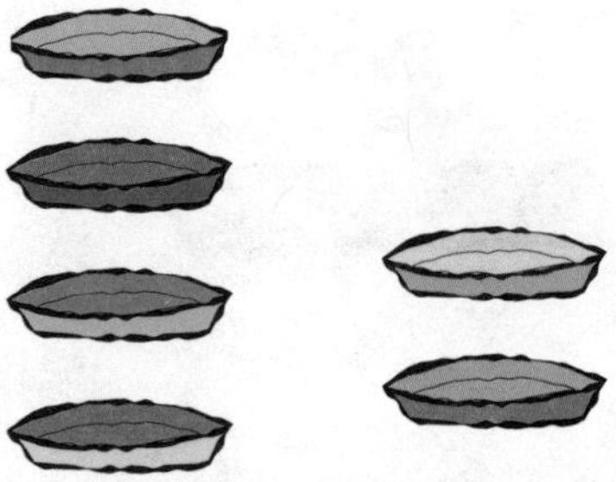

4 dishes   2 dishes

One _____ ran fast, but

four _____ were not fast.

1 fox   4 foxes

520

6 Choose the correct phrase to match the picture. Print the words under the picture.

two dresses
three bunches
one bank

one fan
two foxes
one frog

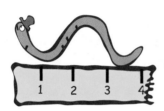

six inches
four inches
one inch

two glasses
one glass
three glasses

1 Follow the letters to connect the dots to make a picture.

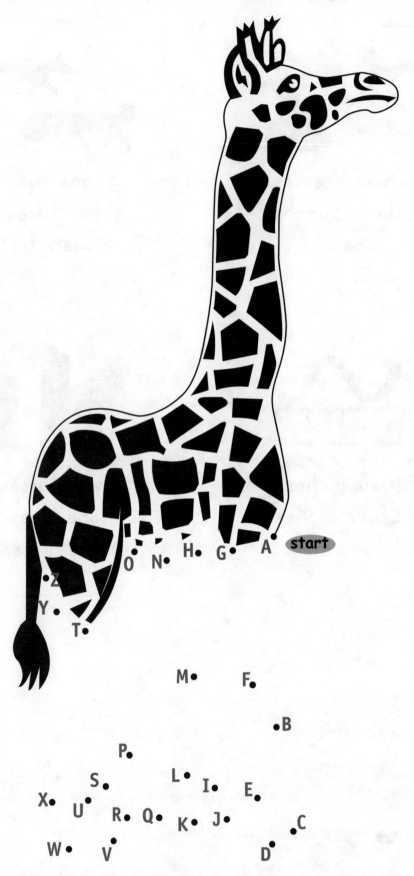

start

O N• H• G A

•Z

Y•

T•

M• F•

•B

P•

S• L• I• E

X• U• R• Q• K• J• •C

W• V• D•

Rule: When a word ends in y, its plural is formed by changing the y to i and adding es.

Example: cry - cries, baby - babies, party - parties.

① Put a circle around the pictures that show plurals (or more than one).

② Spell the word beside the picture where there are two or more objects in the picture. Change the y to i and add es.

1 dolly   3 _____

3 **Spell the words beside each picture where there are two or more objects in the picture. Change the y to i and add es.**

1 baby   2 _____

1 cherry   3 _____

1 cry   3 _____

1 party   2 _____

1 kitty   3 _____

4 **Draw a line from the phrase to the picture it matches.**

two babies crying

three ladies sitting

four puppies running

two happy dollies

read the funnies

5 **Choose and print the correct word to complete the sentence.**

1. We had three _____ on the plate.

candy
candies

2. Dick went to two _____ .

party
parties

3. Three _____ ran to the gate.

puppy
puppies

4. Both _____ are in the crib.

baby
babies

6 **Choose the correct phrase to match the picture. Print the words under the picture.**

two dogs
three lunches
two babies

_____

- - - - - - - - - - - - - - - -

one bus
three ladies
two bikes

_____

- - - - - - - - - - - - - - - -

two kitties
one dress
three bodies

_____

- - - - - - - - - - - - - - - -

_____

one puppy
one bird flies
one baby

_____

- - - - - - - - - - - - - - - -

_____

1 **Put a circle around the pictures that show plurals.**

2 **Underline the pictures that show plurals.**

③ **Put an x on the pictures that do not show plurals.**

④ **Draw a line from the plural word to the word that means just one (singular).**

boxes   horse

cows   box

punches   baby

babies   bag

blesses   punch

bags   cow

horses   bless

LESSON 111
Review: Plurals: s, es, ies

5 **Print the plural form of the following words. Example:** dog - dogs, dish - dishes, baby - babies, fox - foxes, church - churches, dress - dresses.

cat

hand

pig

bib

fish

wish

fox

box

bench

perch

dress

press

cry

baby

6 Read the sentences. Draw a line from the picture to the sentence it matches. Underline all the words that are plural.

The boys play
in the yard.

The babies will
eat the mush.

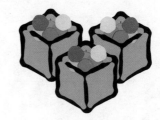

Mom has
pretty skirts.

The benches
are painted green.

The birds
are singing.

The boxes are
full of toys.

sweep

green

sleep

Review Double Vowel Rule: When two vowels are close together, the first one is long (says its own name) and the second one is silent. Examples: gōø̸t, tēø̸m, trāį̸n, bēø̸t.

1 **Look at the pictures below. Put a circle around those that have the long ē sound.**

meet	bee	chain	beet
green	see	sheep	maid
float	wheel	feet	teeth

531

2 On the lines below, print the words that match the picture. Cross out the second vowel and make a straight line over the first vowel to show that it has a long sound.

cheek

creek

greet

green

deep

meet

queen

feed

tree

③ Draw a line from the word to match the picture.

sheep

peek

sheet

breeze

sweep

④ Print the words in alphabetical order.

weed   cheek   peek   tree

1. _____   3. _____

2. _____   4. _____

⑤ Read the make-up words.

sled   breem   creef   wheen

533

6 **Draw a line from the puzzle phrase to the picture it matches.**

three eels
in a tree

a seed on the
queen's heel

sheep in a
deep creek

sweep the
green street

7 **Read the sentences. Draw a line under the one that matches the picture.**

Dad will use a rod when he fishes.

Brad will use a red book when he reads.

Dave will sleep in the street.

Bob ran down the street to meet Lee.

Jill will make green grass for dinner.

Mom can fix beef for lunch.

The candy is too sweet to eat.

Three girls can play the game.

LESSON 112
Review: Double Vowels ee

8 Spell the words under the pictures by filling in the beginning and ending sounds.

_____ ee

_____ ee

_____ ee

_____ ee

_____ ee

_____ ee

_____ ee

_____ ee

9 **Print the words that rhyme.**

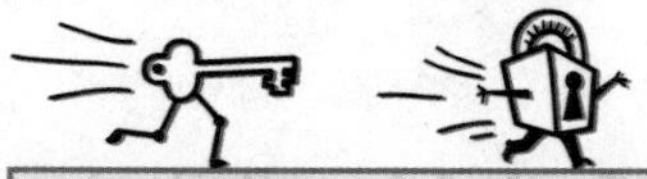

see	creep	creek	peel	need
peek	feel	feed	free	beep
deed	tree	peep	sleek	reel

wheel _____ _____ _____

seed _____ _____ _____

sleep _____ _____ _____

cheek _____ _____ _____

bee _____ _____ _____

10 **Draw a picture of something from the word bank above.**

meet

coast

1. Put a circle around the pictures that have the long ō sound. Put a square around the pictures that have the long ē sound.

boat

beet

feet

float

green

groan

sleep

soap

Review: Double Vowels & Apostrophe

2 **Print the words from the word bank in the columns.**

coat	weep	feed	creep	coal	goat
seed	coach	feet	groan	foal	three

Long ō Sound

Long ē Sound

③ **Print the correct word on the lines in the sentences.**

1. The baby can _____ to the steps.

creep
sleep

2. We saw a _____ eat the corn.

goat
groan

3. The man made a _____ after lunch.

speech
teeth

4. The _____ helped the team play.

coach
catch

④ **Print the words that rhyme.**

| goat | peep | creep | float | seep | boat |

coat _____ _____ _____

deep _____ _____ _____

5 **Spell the words by filling in the double vowel oa or ee under the pictures below.**

g___t   f___d   t___d

s___p   r___st   b___t

ch___k   str___t   r___d

540

This mark ' is an apostrophe.

It is used before the **s** at the end of a word to show that something belongs to one person or thing. This is called possession. It is used as **s'** to show that something belongs to two or more persons or things.

Examples: (One person or thing)

This shirt belongs to Bob. ⟶ This is Bob's shirt

The cat has yellow fur. ⟶ The cat's fur is yellow.

Jack has a red car. ⟶ Jack's car is red.

6 **Change and print the following sentences to show possession of one person or thing. Be sure to use an apostrophe.**

1. The bird has blue wings.

   _____

   The _____ wings are blue.

2. Jack has a big coat.

   _____

   _____ coat is big.

3. The old man has a bent leg.

   _____

   The old _____ leg is bent.

1 **Change and print the following sentences to show possession of two or more persons or things. Be sure to use an apostrophe.**

1. The three dogs have old houses.

The three _____ houses are old.

2. All of the goats have sharp horns.

All of the _____ horns are sharp.

3. The birds have nests in the trees.

The _____ nests are in the trees.

train

mail

seal

āı ēa

① **Put a circle around the pictures that have the** long ā **sound. Put a square around the pictures that have the** long ē **sound.**

grain　　　meat　　　beat　　　stain

speak　　　snail　　　queen　　　team

2 **Print the words from the word bank in the** long ā **or** long ē **rows.**

| Dean | quail | real | bean | rail | deal |
| train | trail | meal | rain | seam | mail |

Long ā sound

_____ _____ _____

_____ _____ _____

_____ _____ _____

Long ē sound

_____ _____ _____

_____ _____ _____

_____ _____ _____

3 **Print the correct word on the line to complete the sentence.**

_____

1. It is fun to ride on a _____ .

train
rain

_____

2. Jean saw a mother _____ .

quail
trail

544

4 **Spell the words by filling in the double vowels ai or ea.**

s____t   m____   tr____n   r____n

m____l   s____l   s____l

tr____t   s____t   b____t

545

5 Change and print the following sentences to show possession of one person or thing. Be sure to use an apostrophe.

1. The baby has a little bottle.

_____

- - - - - - - - - -

The _____ bottle is little.

2. Jim has a dog for a pet.

_____

- - - - - - - - - -

_____ pet is a dog.

3. The dog has a leg that hurts.

_____

- - - - - - - - - -

The _____ leg is hurt.

6 Print the correct word on the line to complete the sentence.

1. You can _____ the cards.   meal   deal

2. Faith will _____ the letters in the box.   mail   sail

3. The _____ will plan to win the game.   team   tame

546

LESSON 115
Review: All Double Vowels

1. Look at the pictures below. Put a circle around those that have the long ā sound.

2. Look at the pictures below. Put a circle around those that have the long ē sound.

3 Look at the pictures below. Put a circle around those that have the long ō sound.

4 Read the make-up words.

claip   steeb   greap   sloaj

5 Draw a line from the puzzle phrase to the picture it matches.

a train
on a tree

the meat
on a chair

jeans on
a goat

a boat on
a wheel

548

6 On the lines below, print the words that match the pictures. Cross out the second vowel, and make a straight line over the first vowel to show that it has a long sound.

coal	creek	road	tree
cheek	maid	speak	rain	chain

_____

_____

_____

7 Print the correct word on the lines in the sentence.

1. Jane has _____ that are pink.

2. The _____ have grass to eat.

3. I see a ship that _____ on the lake.

4. The _____ was on the rail.

5. Don has a _____ on the bus.

6. It is too deep to swim in the _____ .

7. Gail went out in the _____ and got wet.

8. The _____ will float when we ride in it.

cheeks
cheers

sheep
ship

floats
flats

train
trap

seat
seed

creek
slip

ran
rain

bait
boat

⑧ **Spell the words by filling in the double vowels** ee, oa, ea **or** ai.

tr ___ r ___ d b ___ n

___ t ___ l b ___ t f ___ t

s ___ t s ___ d ___ p

c ___ ch s ___ l t ___ st

551

This mark ' is an apostrophe.

It is used before the s at the end of a word to show that something belongs to one person or thing. This is called possession. It is used as s' to show that something belongs to two or more persons or things.

Example: (One person or thing)

This ship belongs to Tom. → This is Tom's ship.

The dog has brown fur. → The dog's fur is brown.

Bill had a blue hat. → Bill's hat is blue.

9 Change and print the following sentences to show possession of two or more persons or things. Be sure to use an apostrophe.

1. The four dogs sleep in big beds.

    _____

    - - - - - - - - - -

    The four _____ beds are big.

2. All of the cats have soft fur.

    _____

    - - - - - - - - - -

    All of the _____ fur is soft.

3. The hens have nests in the pen.

    _____

    - - - - - - - - - -

    The _____ nests are in the pen.

clay

bay

Kay

The digraphs in the words below follow the same double vowel rule: The first vowel is long and the second one is silent, as in the word plāy.

① **Look at the pictures below. Put a circle around those that have the long ā sound.**

tray

jay

bug

play

pray

trap

spray

Kay

553

2 On the lines below, print the words that match the picture. Cross out the second vowel y̸ and make a straight line over the first vowel ā to show it has the long sound of ā.

Fay   tray   pray

pay   Kay   spray

clay   stay   gray

3 Read the make-up words.

snay   tay   glay   chay

4 **Print the words that rhyme.**

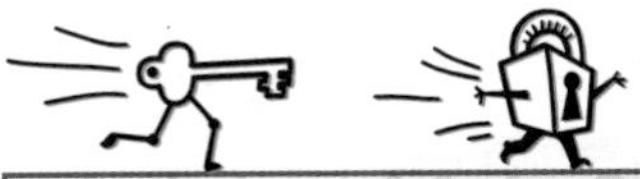

beet	mast	take	rest	deed	say	tug
bay	lug	feet	cast	lake	nest	need
test	heed	lay	rug	greet	last	bake

play

meet

best

past

feed

cake

bug

5 **Draw a line from the puzzle phrase to the picture it matches.**

a weed
on a tray

a jay in the clay

spray the hay

lost the way
to the bay

6 **Spell the words under the pictures by filling in the ay sound.**

J_____   tr_____   cl_____   pl_____

7 **Put the words in alphabetical order.**

day   stay   clay   May

1._____   3._____

2._____   4._____

556

8 **Read the sentences. Draw a line under the one that matches the picture. Print the correct sentence on the lines below.**

Jay can play the game.
Jay can play the tray.

The sheep will pray and then eat.
The sheep will eat the hay.

9 **Read the sentences. Draw a line under the one that matches the picture. Print the correct sentence on the lines below.**

Fay had a good day in her boat at the bay.
Fay had a clay day with her boat at the bay.

_____

- -

_____

- -

We saw a lady with green hair.
We saw a lady with gray hair.

_____

- -

_____

- -

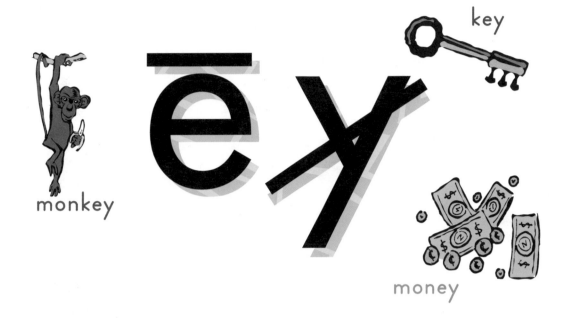

key

monkey

money

The digraphs in the words below follow the same
double vowel rule. The first vowel in the digraph is long
and says its own name. The second one is silent, as in monkēy.

1 **Look at the pictures below. Put a circle around those that have the**
long ē sound.

monkey   donkey   vest   money

valley   hockey   man   key

559

② On the lines below, print the words that match the pictures. Cross out the second vowel of the digraph and make a straight line over the first vowel to show that it has the long ē sound.

key   monkey   money

hockey   valley   donkey

③ Look at the pictures. Listen for the long ē sound. Draw a line from the picture to the word that rhymes.

donkey

see

deep

seen

4 **Read the sentences with your teacher. Draw a line from the picture to the sentence that tells about the word.**

1. This is another name for dimes, nickels, quarters and dollars.

2. This is a game that is played on the ice.

3. This is an animal that lives in the zoo.

4. This is a place between two or more mountains.

5. This is something that will open or lock doors.

6. This is an animal that usually lives on a farm.

hockey

money

valley

monkey

key

donkey

5 **Print the words from Exercise 4.**

6 **Read the make-up words.**

rey   bley   stey   chey

7 **Draw a line from the puzzle phrase to the picture it matches.**

a donkey
in a tree

a monkey
with money

a key for a fish

a hockey player
with a football

8 **Print the words in alphabetical order.**

money key donkey valley

1._____   3._____

2._____   4._____

562

hockey

pray

The digraphs ey and ay follow the double vowel rule.
The first vowel is long and the second one
is silent, as in the words kēÿ and grāÿ.

1 Put a circle around the words that have the long ā sound.
Put a square around the words that have the long ē sound.

play   key   clay   x–ray

money   monkey   day   donkey

563

2 **Choose the correct word to complete the sentence.**

1. I get up in the morning each _____ .

day
pay

2. The dish was made of red _____ .

clay
may

3. The brown _____ lives in the zoo.

monkey
money

4. We are wet from the _____ of the hose.

spray
stay

5. Dad has the _____ to buy a car.

money
many

6. May has a pretty _____ dress.

gray
gay

7. The men can play the _____ game.

hockey
honey

8. We went to church to _____ .

pray
play

564

3 **Draw a line from the picture to the word it matches.**

donkey

spray

monkey

hockey

pray

tray

x-ray

play

4 **Finish spelling the words under the pictures by writing the correct letters ay or ey.**

donk___   monk___   pr___

x–r___   k___   h___

spr___   hock___   tr___

pl___   mon___   hon___

Review: An apostrophe is used before the 's in a word to show that something belongs to one person or thing. It is used after the s' to show that something belongs to two or more persons or things.

5 **Change and print the following sentences to show possession of one person or thing. Be sure to use an apostrophe.**

1. The tail of the monkey is long.

2. The rays of the sun are hot.

3. The handles of the tray are black.

6 **Change and print the following sentences to show possession of two or more persons or things. Be sure to use an apostrophe.**

1. Both tots have new toys.

2. The moles have homes in the dirt.

3. The gas tanks of all the cars are full.

4. Both boys have gray monkeys.

LESSON 119
Diphthong ow

snow

howl

The diphthong ow is a set of two sounds blended, as in the word cow. It also makes the long ō sound you hear in the word slow.

1 Look at the pictures below. Put a circle around the picture if it has the ow sound as in cow.

crown   owl   frown   goat

clown   howl   pen   cow

2 **Draw a line from the picture to the word it matches.**

plow

town

brown

clown

crown

cow

3 **Look at the pictures below. Put a circle around the picture if it has the** long ō **sound as in** slow.

④ **Draw a line from the picture to the word it matches.**

crow

show

snow

elbow

bowl

throw

⑤ **Print the correct word on the line in the sentence.**

1. Dad will _____the grass   mow
   in the back yard.   morning

                                                  window
2. Owen fell down and hurt his _____. elbow

                                                  yard
3. We saw pretty colors in the _____. rainbow

                                                  throw
4. Don can _____ the ball in the game. grow

                                                  snow
5. We will go to the _____to see the clown. show

6. The boys and girls will play in the _____ snow

   with the sleds.   show

6 **Circle the word your teacher reads.**

crow　mow　brown	frown　show　throw
clown　how　slow	grow　crown　elbow

7 **Print the correct word on the line in the sentence.**

1. Mom drove to _____ in a red truck.

town
down

2. Jake has some short _____ pants.

brown
crown

3. The wings on the _____ were broken.

out
owl

4. The queen's _____ had many stones in it.

frown
crown

5. Mike, the _____, made us smile.

clown
cow

6. I want to see _____ Mom makes the cake.

how
plow

572

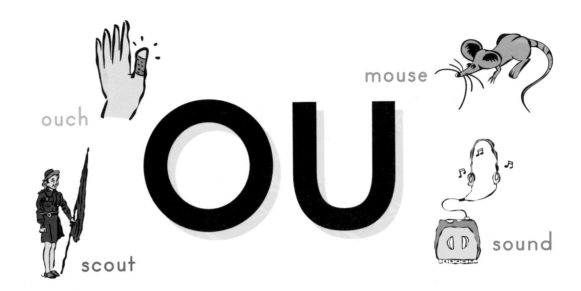

ouch

mouse

scout

sound

The diphthong ou is the blended vowel sound
you hear in the word out.

1 **Put a circle around the pictures that have the ou sound, as in out.**

mouse

ouch

swim

scout

count

cloud

loud

north

② **Print the ou sound in the words under the pictures.**

cl____d   m____nt   r____nd

____ch   fl____r   c____ch

m____th   ____tside   s____nd

574

3 **Print the correct word on the line in the sentence.**

1. Jane has a _____ of grapes.

   pound
   sound

2. She will take _____ dog for
   a fast run.

   out
   our

3. The cat will _____ when he
   wants to catch a mouse.

   crouch
   couch

4. We made a _____ mark on
   the chart.

   round
   south

5. The rat made a hole in the _____ .

   ground
   ouch

6. The apple was too _____ for
   our mouths.

   sour
   found

7. The _____ will help set
   up the tents.

   scout
   flour

575

The diphthong ou blended together can also make the sound we hear in the word you.

④ **Print the ou sound in the words under the pictures.**

c____gar   s____p

gr____p   w____nd

⑤ **Put a square around the pictures that have the sound you hear in the word you.**

LESSON 120
Diphthong ou

6 **Print the correct word on the line in the sentences.**

1. _____ are to fill in the words
on the lines.

Yet
You

2. Mom can fix some _____ for
our lunch.

soup
sound

3. The _____ can bite you.

cougar
cage

7 **Print the sentences below. Be sure to use a capital letter at the beginning. Finish your sentence with a period or question mark.**

i like to do a lot of reading

what do you like to do for fun

577

Review nouns: A noun names a person, place or thing.

8 Read each noun that names a thing. Draw a line to the picture
it matches.

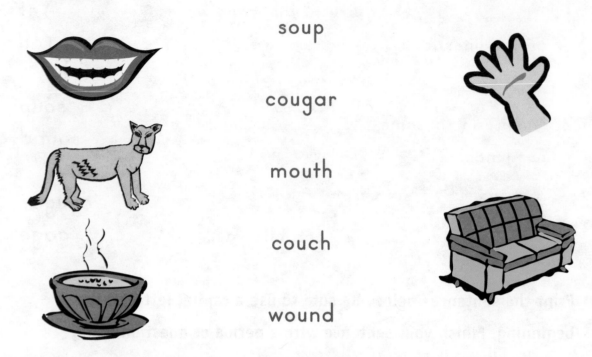

soup

cougar

mouth

couch

wound

9 Read each noun that names a thing. Draw a line to the picture
it matches.

snow

elbow

cow

crown

clown

578